CW00858832

A CATHOLIC BIBLE STORYBOOK
FOR YOUNG CHILDREN
With Activities

By Marion Sauer

Illustrated by Theresa Brekan

BOOK 1

A Catholic Bible Storybook Series For Young Children
Book 1

To God, with thanksgiving for my grandchildren and great-grandchildren for the beautiful gifts that they are, for the love and joy that they bring.

A Note to Parents:

"Let the little children come to me," Jesus says in Matthew 19:14. God calls children to himself with tenderness and mercy. We are privileged to help plant seeds of faith in our children, pray for them and watch God's grace work in their lives.

The story of creation, the beginning of all things made from nothing by the spoken Word of God, is the beginning of the salvation story depicted in the Bible. The story in Genesis tells us that God created the world as a gift to mankind. He placed our first parents, Adam and Eve, in the Garden of Eden where they lived in harmony with Him. Scripture tells us that God loves all that He has created, and He created everything good. Even though our first parents sinned, God loved Adam and Eve and their children, protected them and taught them His ways. God promised salvation through one of their offspring who would destroy the evil serpent.

A Catholic Bible Storybook Series for Young Children introduces children to major Bible stories in God's plan of salvation. These colorful stories are simplified retellings of Bible stories. They provide an opportunity for families to explore together the beautiful mystery of God's presence in our lives. They are ideal for reading aloud and sharing family time with fun activities that help children understand God's love and purpose for them in their everyday life. Concepts from the Catechism of the Catholic Church are included to help bring home lessons from the stories.

Scripture references are listed for parents who want to read the accounts as they appear in the Bible. *Catechism of the Catholic Church* (CCC) references are listed for further study.

Genesis 1-3

"In the beginning God created the heavens and the earth."

Genesis 1:1

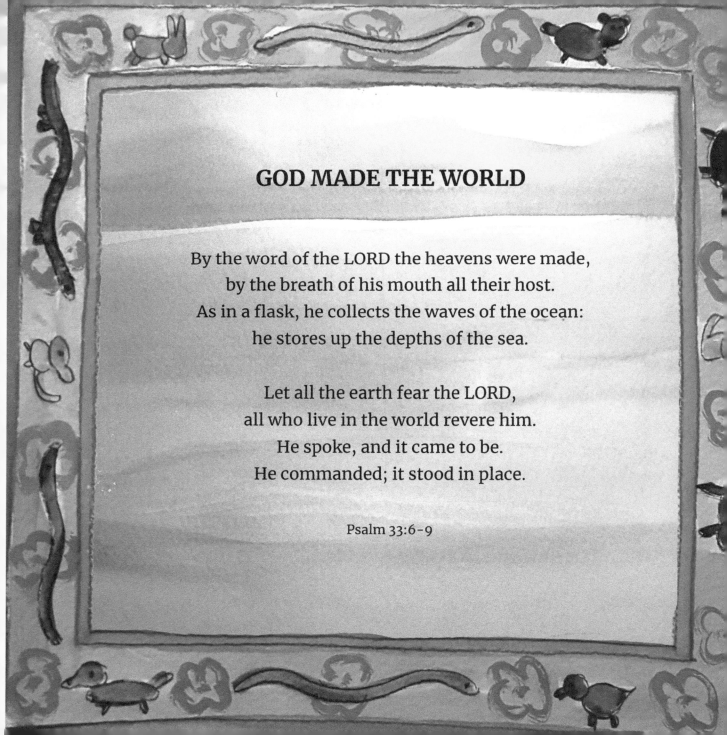

GOD MADE THE WORLD

By the word of the LORD the heavens were made,
by the breath of his mouth all their host.
As in a flask, he collects the waves of the ocean:
he stores up the depths of the sea.

Let all the earth fear the LORD,
all who live in the world revere him.
He spoke, and it came to be.
He commanded; it stood in place.

Psalm 33:6-9

Long ago, before the world began, God lived in a spiritual realm full of light, full of glory, full of love and beauty. His love was so great, He wanted to create a new world for a new family.

Out of nothing at all God began to create, at first in swirling darkness.
"Let there be light!" God joyfully shouted, and brightness lit all around.
He called the light day, and the dark He called night. God rejoiced in the
first morning light.

God declared on the second day, "Let there be sky between the waters to separate the two." A great sky rose high above the water below, and there was new air as a new wind blew.

On the third day God's powerful words rang clear, "Now, let the dry land appear." Mountains and flatlands rose up from the seas bringing forth grasses, bushes and fruit-bearing trees. God saw it all and was very pleased.

The fourth day God said, "Let lights of all kinds shine in the sky." The sun brightened the day and the moon glistened at night. The evening sky twinkled with stars and planets and colorful lights. They worked together to turn the seasons and mark passing time. God was happy with what He had done, but more was still to come.

The fifth day came and God cheerfully exclaimed, "Let the earth bring forth its creatures." The oceans swelled with big and small fish and sea animals of many kinds. The skies abounded with colorful birds and everything that flies. God said to the creatures He had made, "Be fruitful and multiply."

On the sixth day God commanded, "Let more come to fill the land." In forests and fields animals were born, and beasts roamed free. They could climb, swim, run, jump, and swing from trees. They howled and growled, barked and bellowed, clucked and crowed, squeaked and screeched. Bees made intricate honeycombs, and insects swarmed in underground homes. "This is good!" God joyfully said. But the day was young, the best was yet to come.

On this special day God's heart rejoiced. "Let us make mankind in our own image," He said, scooping clay from the earth. He formed the clay into a man and gave him the breath of life. Then God took a rib from the man to make a woman to be his wife. God called the man Adam and the woman Eve. He stamped his image of love on their hearts, their souls were filled with His light. He was their Heavenly Father, and they were His earthly son and daughter.

God placed Adam and Eve in the garden of Eden, blessing them with His love. "Have many children," God proclaimed, "and take care of the world I made." He gave them earth as their home, all creatures to care for, and delicious plants for food. God looked with delight and joyfully said, "Ah, this is very, very good!"

On the seventh day God's world was complete, blessed and beautifully made. As His new family rose with the morning sun, God rested from all he had done.

Adam and Eve

Adam and Eve, the first people God made, lived happily as husband and wife. They drank from cold streams, enjoyed plentiful food, and shared God's abundant life.

"Eat from the trees in the Garden of Eden, all except one," God said. "In the middle of the Garden, the one growing tall, you may not have at all."

One warm sunny day, Eve's heart rejoiced as she picked luscious fruits from the trees. In an instant she stopped as a dark shadow dropped across her winding path. She looked up and saw the one tree growing tall, and was startled by an eerie call. "Eeeeve...ssss!"

"Ssss... sss!" hissed a slimy green snake, hiding among the leaves. "Eat the fruit, eat the fruit, eat the fruit from the forbidden tree. It's not bad; it's good for you. Eat it, and you will see... Ssssss."

Eve heard the snake, saw the fruit and greatly desired to taste it. She reached her hand for the forbidden fruit and stuffed it into her mouth. "Adam," she called, "Take some, too," and handed him a piece. He swallowed the fruit, felt suddenly cold, his trembling wouldn't cease. "Ooooh!"

"Adam, where are you?" they heard God call in His strong fatherly voice. "Why did you eat the forbidden fruit I told you to stay away from?" Sad and confused, Adam and Eve covered themselves with leaves. And they watched in wonder as God cast away the snake who caused such grief.

"Now you must leave the Garden of Eden," they sadly heard God say. "Go and learn to live and work, and I will always lead you. Some day your offspring will come and destroy the evil one." They left the Garden and built their tents in a land toward the East. Watched over by God, they learned to trust Him and tried their very best.

Adam and Eve worked the hard soil to grow vegetables, grains and herbs. They kept warm in winter with coats God made them out of animal skins. They bathed in cool waters in the heat of summer and enjoyed shade from the trees. Then Eve happily cried "God blessed me again!" as she gave birth to her first son, Cain.

Adam and Eve had another child, Abel, and then many more. Their children grew and had choices to make, for good or for bad. Some honored God and did good deeds, and some did not. Yet, Adam and Eve taught their family to always give thanks to the Lord, "Thank you, God, for giving us life and the beautiful world as a gift for us all."

I Can See

1 Planet   5 Snow Capped Mountains   2 Alligators   2 Dolphins Jumping   2 Cherry Trees   2 Waterfa

8 Red Flowers

2 Flying Fish

2 Butterflies
with Blue Wings

2 Snowflakes

2 Bees Making
Honeycombs

1 Penguin

FAMILY ACTIVITIES

God Made You

CCC 357, 1029, 2270

Scripture verse: Psalm 139:13-14
For it was you who formed my inmost being,
Knit me together in my mother's womb,
I thank you who wonderfully made me;
how wonderful are your works,
which my soul knows well!

Ideas to share:
God made you! You are a child of God. He loves you and gave you life. You are made in God's image. No one else is just like you, or looks exactly the way you do.

God gave you a soul to know and love Him, and care for others, too. Then live with joy forever with Him in the Kingdom of Heaven. Let's talk about the special ways that God made you.

Activity:
Lie on a large length of butcher paper. Mom or dad trace around your body. With markers or crayons draw your face and hair and color them the way you look. Draw clothes and color them in with your favorite colors.

Let's pray:
Dear Lord, thank You for making us and loving us. Help us use our gifts and talents to share Your love and to help others. Amen.

God made the world for us to enjoy. There is so much to see and do. God gave us our family to help us grow and learn many things that we didn't know. Let's listen and learn and try new things, exploring adventures that life brings.

Favorite Things to Do

CCC 2207, 2228

Scripture verse: Collosians 3:17
And whatever you do, in word or deed, do everything in the name of the Lord Jesus, giving thanks to God the Father through Him.

Ideas to share:
We see blue skies dappled with clouds, like cotton balls in summer, whirling golden leaves on gusts of wind in fall, icy silver snowflakes swirling in winter, rain splashing on our window pains in spring.

We romp through forests and stomp through puddles, dig tunnels in sand where tiny crabs dive. We can race uphill and downhill, roll through leaves, and say thank you to God for all that He gives.

God gave you gifts and talents. There is no one just like you. What do you like to do?

Activity:
With others in your family, make collages of your favorite things to do. Mom or dad divide paper or poster boards with lines into four squares. Then each family member draw pictures (or glue cut-outs from magazines) in each square showing favorite things to do. Hold up and share the finished products!

Let's pray:
Thank You, Lord, for our family and others who teach us and help us to grow. Help us to do our very best each day. Bless our work and our play. Amen.

Caring for the World CCC 373, 2457

Scripture verse: Genesis 1:28
God blessed them, and God said to them, "…have dominion over the fish of the sea and over the birds of the air and over every living thing that moves upon the earth."

Ideas to share: The world is full of the glory of God, reflecting his beauty on land, sea and sky. Everything living, animals and plants, need our special care. In the city or the country, wherever you live, what are things you can do to care for the environment and animals, too?

Family Activity: Have a family picnic in the park. Talk about the beauty of God's creation. Enjoy the outdoors!

Let's Pray: Dear Heavenly Father, thank You for creating the world as a wonderful gift for us all. Show us ways to take good care of our beautiful world. Amen.

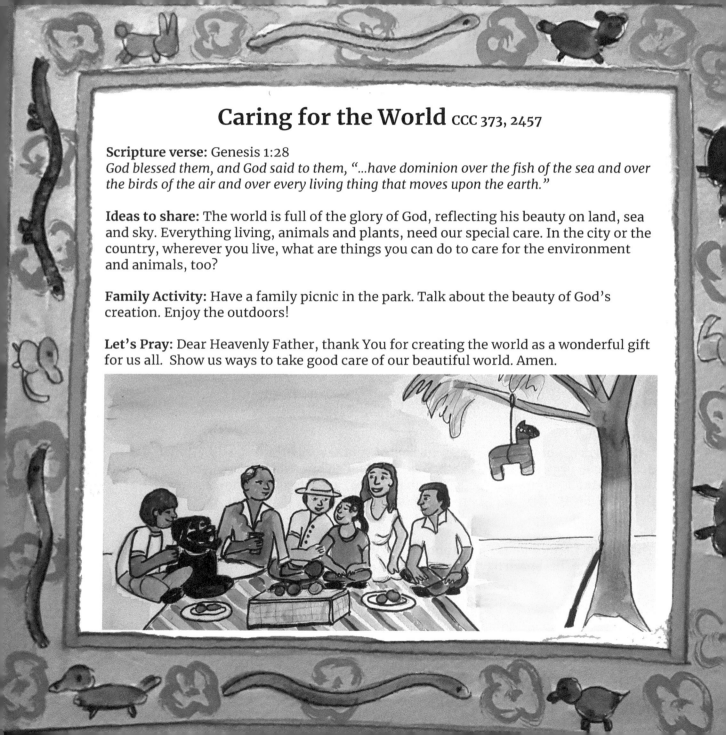

Caring for Ourselves and Others CCC 1823, 2208

Scripture verse: 1 Timothy 6:18
They are to do good, to be rich in good works, generous, and ready to share.

Ideas to share: God gives us our families to love and share, and learn to treat other people with care. He gives us a heart to help one another, to care for ourselves and to care for others. Let's talk about ways to be kind and good, helping others, as we should.

Family Activity: Make cookies with mom. Go with your family to visit someone who needs cheering up, is sick or lonely. Give them the cookies and share a big smile!

Let's pray: Dear Lord, You love everyone in the world, for You made us all. Thank You especially for our family and those who love us. Help us to do good for others and to take care of ourselves and each other. Amen.

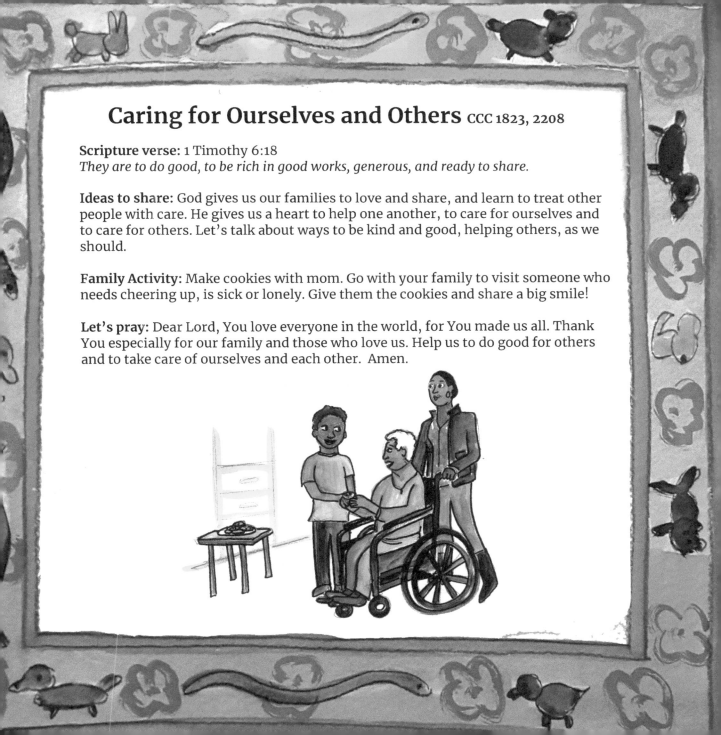

A poem to share...

The Canticle of Brother Sun

Be praised, my Lord, with all Your creatures,
Especially Sir Brother Sun,
By whom You give us the light of day!
And he is beautiful and radiant with great splendor.
Of you, Most High, he is a symbol.

Be praised, my Lord, for Sister Moon and the Stars!
In the sky You formed them bright and lovely and fair.

Be praised, My Lord, for Brother Wind
And for the Air and cloudy and clear and all Weather,
By which you give sustenance to Your creatures!

Be praised, My Lord, for Sister Water,
Who is very useful and humble and lovely and chaste!

Be praised, my Lord, for Brother Fire,
By whom You give us light at night,
And he is beautiful and merry and mighty and strong!

Be praised, my Lord, for our Sister Mother Earth,
Who sustains and governs us,
And produces fruits with colorful flowers and leaves!

Praise and bless my Lord and thank Him
And serve Him with great humility!

St. Francis of Assisi

Lightning Source UK Ltd.
Milton Keynes UK
UKHW050901030720
365929UK00003B/80